French Dolls in Color

by

Patricia R. Smith

COLLECTOR BOOKS

DEDICATION

This little book is dedicated to Marlowe Cooper, who as a collector of very beautiful dolls, does not mind sharing her dolls and information. We thank her for her friendship, which means so much to us.

CREDITS

All photos by Dwight F. Smith unless noted.
THANK YOU to the following for their help in making this a book filled with beautiful dolls:

Louella Alvenslaben • Photos by Ted Long
Marlowe Cooper • Photos by Don Allen
Kathryn Fain • Photo by herself
Sherry Garcia • Photos by M. E. Lora
Jeanne Gregg • Photos by O. D. Gregg
Jeanne Haskins • Photos by Ted Long
Clarice Kemper • Photos by herself •
Jill Koons • Photos by Penny Pendlebury
Roberta Lago • Photo by Ted Long
Barbra Jean Male • Photos by Mike Male
Margaret McDonald • Photos by Ted Long
Jay Minter • Photos by Dwight Smith
Joy Muir • Photos by Venta
Mary Nutt • Photos by M. E. Lora
Cynthia Orgeron • Photos by M. E. Lora and Venta •
Mary Partridge • Photos by Brother and Ted Long
Penny Pendlebury • Photos by Penny
Karen Penner • Photos by Dwight Smith
Ethel Stewart • Photos by Ted Long
Burnice Wallen • Photos by Ted Long
Delores Ward • Photos by Venta, Neil & William

Additional copies of this book may be ordered from:

COLLECTOR BOOKS
P.O. Box 3009
Paducah, Kentucky 42001

Please add .50¢ to help defray shipping charges

ISBN: 0-89145-101-3

CONTENTS

FRENCH DOLLS

French dolls are more often referred to as Bébé which is a term to indicate a child between the age of eight and thirteen. One of the most desirable Bébés is the Bru (Company founded in 1866). The early Brus have beautifully modeled shoulder plates that have the breasts of a young adolescent, with even the nipples lightly tinted, as well as unusually fine modelling of the heads.

Very early Brus have kid gusseted bodies with bisque lower arms. The Bru hands are a thing of beauty unto themselves, and no other doll can match the quality of these hands. The Bru Jnes generally have kid over wood bodies with wood lower legs. The latest Brus have jointed composition bodies.

The early Bru was marked with a circle and dot that is a deep indentation and is where the mechanism would have entered the head if it had been scheduled to be made into a "nursing" Bru with open mouth. These circle-dot Brus have open/closed mouths and some with tiny molded teeth. Some will have just a portion of the circle and dot and are referred to as crescent-dot Brus.

The majority of the early Brus had caracul/lambskin wigs and many were removed by early owners and replaced with other wigs. It is important to retain the originalness of any doll and if the wigs must be changed, the old one should be placed in a sack and pinned to the underneath of the back of the dress, that way a future owner who may prefer the original can do so.

The early all kid Bru bodies became "slouched" or assumed a crouching position as the cork filling shifted and no "movement" was attainable. The arms have wires and can be posed slightly. It was due to this that Bru started to carve the wooden lower legs and jointed the knees and elbows and this enabled the doll to sit and move its arms (1873). The later Bru is on a wood and composition body with bisque socket head. These Brus with composition bodies came with either open or closed mouths.

The original clothes of a Bru doll are a work of art and mostly hand sewn. Silk brocades, satin, lace and very fine wools were used. Most dolls were dressed in the era made and were miniatures of the current child's styles. Originally dressed dolls can generally be dated by these styles.

Bru was the most exclusive of the French doll makers and these dolls were very expensive at that time, and generally were only found in the arms of a child with wealthy parents. The Bru company attempted to make dolls that were not successful and are ultra-rare to collectors today. They include Bebe Gourmand (1881) with pull strings in the back of the head and was advertised as being able to "eat and digest food", a doll that appeared to breathe and Bebe 'Le Dormeur' with eyelids that closed over the eyes. The most common and often found Bru "that did something" is the "Nursing Bru" with a bulb inside the head and an operating mechanism in the back (mold hole where the uncut holes formed a "circle and dot").

Despite the beauty and quality of the Bru dolls they were only awarded silver medals at the Toy Expositions and these medals were for the clothing, until the company moved into the hands of H. Chevrot, who kept the name of Bru Jne & Cie. Under the direction of Chevrot Bru dolls received many Gold medals.

Jumeau was the largest competitor to Bru and out advertised the Bru firm. Because the German dolls were much cheaper, the French firm's only chance at surviving was beautifully dressed and high quality dolls were directed at the upper-middle class in Europe, England and America and Trade Exhibits in all these countries helped in promoting the French dolls.

Jumeau advertised "Bébé Jumeau" as early as the 1860's but these early Jumeau were what collectors now call "French Fashions". They actually were lady dolls and play dolls and are found on both all kid bodies as well as wood articulated bodies. It was in 1879 that the actual Bébé Jumeau was marketed. It was in 1878 at the Paris Exposition that the dolls were first shown. They received the medal of Honor (Gold) and from this the bodies are stamped with the Medaille d'or.

One of the most remarkable characteristics of the Jumeau dolls were their fine, large and luminous eyes. Jumeau trained women for years before they became skilled in blowing these fine glass eyes. It was in 1885 that Jumeau introduced a Bébé with eyelids that closed down over the eyes by a lever in back of the head.

Considered by many collectors to be the most desirable Jumeau is the doll that is referred to as a "Cody Jumeau" or "Long Face Jumeau". Buffalo Bill Cody purchased one and brought it to the U.S.A. and so the name was born.

Closed mouth dolls are rarer than open mouth dolls even if the open mouths with teeth were considered an important advance in doll making and were more expensive to produce due to the extra manufacturing process.

The quality of the Jumeau dolls can vary and the value must be placed on that quality. The German competition caused Jumeau to introduce two dolls in 1892, twenty to fifty percent discount from the regular dolls, but without the firm's name used. Many Jumeau dolls were unmarked with only the body bearing their stamp. Although these "unmarked" Jumeaus are generally easily recognizable, the value is not as high as a marked doll would be. Jumeau produced walking dolls that throw kisses, voice boxes worked by pull strings and even a phonograph talking doll with wax cylinders (1894).

Madame Jumeau supervised the design and making of the doll clothes and some of these examples are among the finest of all dolls.

Not all Jumeau dolls were sold dressed and some, even in original boxes, are found dressed in a simple chemise. A great many of the later Jumeau dolls are found, both with and without boxes, in a flowered cotton dress. The flowers came in several colors, such as blue and rose, and have a pleated hem and puff sleeves.

The most elusive and desirable French dolls are the ones made by A. Thullier and marked with A.T. These dolls also can vary in quality, but most have a hauntingly beautiful expression. These dolls were made between 1875 and 1890. Next would be the dolls marked with an "H". The maker is unknown, but the dolls are rare and beautiful and command a very high price.

The "rarest" of the French dolls are the ones marked A. Marque. The modelling of these heads is unusual and has the look of no other French doll. The bodies are composition and the lower arms are bisque. The bodies are long and thin and the feet are also long and thin. The mouths are closed and one authority states that there are only 21 of these dolls made.

It was in 1885 that the Jules Steiner company entered the doll field and they created more "mechanical" dolls than other makers. The "looks" of Steiner dolls vary greatly with some resembling the Schmitts. The quality varies greatly also. There are Steiners with two rows of teeth, walking Steiners with wheels, crying Steiners with Motchman style bodies and even dolls with a lever mechanism to control the eyes and located just above the ears.

Some of the characteristics of a Steiner are: a pate of purple cardboard instead of the cork pates used by other French makers, fingers of the same length and a big toe that is separate from the others. Some dolls are unmarked and are early examples with most having a pink wash over the eyes. Some Steiner dolls are marked with Le Parisien and some with Bourgoin and a great many are marked with an "A" followed by a number, these are referred to as an "A series Steiner" and bear a resemblance to a Jumeau. The "A" series dolls have a darker and longer eyelash line directly in the corner of the eyes.

Among the other French makers are Rabery and Delphieu with dolls marked with an R.D. and most examples are of excellent quality (there are exceptions). Also, with the mark of E.D. and made by E. Denamur firm, which also had very good quality. Both these marked dolls, both open and closed mouth versions, are rapidly disappearing from the collector market and therefore the prices are increasing.

The Fleischman and Blodel firm originated in Bavaria but also had a branch in Paris. They were the makers of the Eden Bebe, which can be found with both open and closed mouths and vary greatly in quality.

Fernand Gaultier made a great many dolls and the most often

found ones are of the "Lady" type (Fashions). The child dolls from this company are usually fatter of face than other dolls of the period. The dolls from this firm are marked with an F.G., with the earlier examples marked with the F.G. inside a scroll.

As the German makers took more and more of the market away from the higher priced French dolls, the French makers were forced to join into the Societe Francaise de Fabrication de Bébés et Jouets (S.F.B.J.) in 1899. The director of this new organization was Fleischmann and others included Bru, Rabery and Delphieu, Jumeau among others. At first the dolls were produced under their own trade names, but marketing and production was cut and streamlined to try and compete. There was a lowering of standards and a great many of the S.F.B.J. dolls are actually of poor quality. It must be remembered that there are exceptions to everything, and some of the S.F.B.J. period of dolls are exceptions, especially in the 200 series mold numbers.

French dolls are very desirable to the collector because they are rarer, usually of fine quality and when found in original clothes are generally unsurpassed by German made dolls. French dolls command a higher price because of the rarity, especially the early examples, and the closed mouth versions.

HOW TO USE PRICE GUIDE

The determining factor in pricing a bisque doll is the head. The main thing is the quality of the bisque. The best bisque is flawless, both in "depth" of bisque, that is the look of the bisque, not the actual thickness. There must not be any damage to the head, which includes hairline cracks, cracked or broken shoulder plates, eye chips and cracks, mends, repairs and even a chip of a pierced ear plays a part in pricing these dolls.

The most desirable dolls are completely perfect, are original and in original boxes and never played with. But prices based on this assumption are unrealistic as the ratio is an overwhelming 6,000 to 1 against finding a doll in the above stated condition. That leaves 5,999 dolls showing varying degrees of use . . . so the prices are based on perfect, excellent quality of bisque with no defects. Occasionally there will be flecks of what looks like dirt in the bisque of a fine doll and some collectors refuse to buy these dolls unless they are below the asking prices of perfect examples, but if the flecks are few and not detracting the quality of the doll should be considered the same.

Body rubs, a missing finger, a crack in a kid body, a minor repair to the foot, etc. (These are minor, not major damages) play no part in the prices in this book and we have not gone into great detail on the bodies. There are a few dolls (French) that have characters unique to that maker, such as a Bru body, a Steiner and a typical Jumeau body and with a little study a collector can come to recognize if the head is on the correct body. One point is important in regard to bodies. The German makers loved to put in knee detail where the French makers ran the upper leg flat into the lower leg without any knee detail. The French bodies have legs that are jointed at the knee but are flush jointed and the Germans generally had a space between the upper and lower leg.

The first and foremost importance is the condition and the quality of the bisque head of the doll that you are thinking of buying or selling. Collectors set their own prices by what they are willing to pay to get a certain example of a doll to add to their collections. Since allowances must be made in reference to the quality of any bisque head, the scale method of pricing will be used. For example: a doll that is 20″ tall and marked "W-X" would be valued between $2,200 and $2,400 depending on the bisque.

A $50.00
B 100.00
C 150.00
D 200.00
E 250.00
F 300.00
G 350.00
H 400.00
I 450.00
J 500.00
K 600.00
L 700.00
M 800.00
N 900.00
O 1,000.00
P 1,050.00
Q 1,100.00
R 1,200.00
S 1,300.00
T 1,450.00
U 1,700.00
V 1,900.00
W 2,200.00
X 2,400.00
Y 2,700.00
Z 3,000.00
ZA 3,500.00
ZB 4,000.00
ZC 4,500.00
ZD 5,000.00
ZE 5,500.00
ZF 6,000.00
ZG 6,500.00
ZH 7,000.00
ZI 7,500.00
ZJ 8,000.00
ZK 8,500.00
ZL 9,000.00
ZM 9,500.00
ZN 10,000.00

Doll collecting can be a great hobby, with many ways to display dolls. Here is one corner in which Jay and Ralph Minter have utilized a piece of antique furniture and a home made case. Of the two large dolls inside the cases, the one in light blue is a "Long face" Jumeau with closed mouth and the other is an all original, open mouth Jumeau.

ALEXANDRE, HENRI

22″ Phenix Bebe. Ball jointed composition body with straight wrists. Closed mouth. Marked with a ★90. Made by Henri Alexandre. Courtesy Jeanne Haskins. Photo by Ted Long.

R-T

BELTON TYPES

9½″ French Belton type. Head incised: 1. Wood and composition body with straight wrists. Original wig, ears pierced into head. 5¾″ All bisque with swivel neck. Long arms with large hands, thin torso with long thin legs/yellow-orange socks and two strap black shoes. Deep slice in head. Original wig. 5½″ All bisque. Head incised: O. Swivel neck, applied ears, bent arms and molded on black heeled boots with four straps. Courtesy Barbra Jean Male. Photo by Mike Male.

I-K

BELTON TYPES

This photograph shows the detail in the face of the 9½″ Belton type. Closed mouth, multi stroke eyebrows and the ears are pierced into the head. Excellent bisque for such a small doll. Courtesy Barbra Jean Male. Photo by Mike Male.

BELTON TYPES

14½" Belton Type with solid dome head. Jointed body with straight wrists. Unmarked. Pull string talker, says "Mama" and "Papa". Courtesy Jeanne Haskins. Photo by Ted Long.

K-M

BRU

12½" Bru Jne #2. Walking body, brown eyes. Tip of tongue shows in closed mouth. Marked on head and shoulder plate. The clothes may be original. Excellent bisque and these early dolls are difficult to find in this small size. Courtesy Marlowe Cooper. Photo by Don Allen.

ZE-ZG

BRU

13½″ Bru Jne #3. Walking body, brown eyes. Tongue tip shows in closed mouth. Her costume may be original. This is another delightfully excellent quality smaller doll. From the Collection of Marlowe Cooper. Photo by Don Allen.

ZF-ZG

BRU

17″ Bru Jne #5. Marked head, shoulder plate and the wooden Bru body is also marked. Brown eyes and closed mouth with tip of tongue showing. Dressed in a Kate Greenaway style. Courtesy Marlowe Cooper. Photo by Don Allen.

ZG-ZH

BRU

17½″ Bru. Swivel head on deep bisque shoulder plate marked Bru Jne. Pierced ears and kid body and upper arms, with bisque lower arms. Head is marked with a circle and dot and she has an open/closed mouth with molded teeth. Courtesy Jeanne Gregg. Photo by O. D. Gregg.

ZE-ZF

BRU

17″ Early Bru marked with a full "circle and dot". All kid body with bisque lower arms. All original except wig. Closed mouth. (Author) Photo by Dwight Smith.

ZE-ZF

BRU

17″ Bisque socket head on bisque shoulder plate. Kid over wood body with bisque lower arms and wood lower legs. Open/closed mouth and pierced ears. All original. Marks; Bru Jne, on head. Bru Jne 5 and No. 5 over shoulder plate. (Author) Photo by Dwight Smith.

ZG-ZH

BRU

Unmarked 18″ tall Bru. She only has an 11 on head. Socket head on bisque shoulder plate with kid body and bisque lower arms. Pierced ears and human hair wig. Set brown eyes and closed mouth. Courtesy Jeanne Gregg. Photo by O. D. Gregg.

Y-Z

BRU

19″ Nursing Bru and all original. Bébé Teteur nursing doll's head and kid body patented by Casimir Bru Jr. 1879. Has full kid body with bisque lower arms. Marks: Depose, on front shoulder plate. Head is marked: Bru Jne/5/Bru. Wire formed upper arms. Open mouth/nurser. Courtesy Jeanne Gregg. Photo by O. D. Gregg.

Z-ZA

BRU

19″ Bru Jne #6 with blue-grey eyes. Marked head, shoulder plate and has walking body. Old costume and original wig. From the collection of Marlowe Cooper. Photo by Don Allen.

ZG-ZH

BRU

20″ Closed mouth and ball jointed composition body. Marks; Bru Jne R. Courtesy Burnice Wallen. Photo by Ted Long.

ZB-ZC

BRU

21″ Bru Jne #7. She is marked on the head, shoulder plate and has a paper label. She has a walking body and brown eyes. The tip of the tongue shows in her closed mouth. Her dress is one cut down from a child's dress and the hat has Paris label (Judith Barbier) Courtesy Marlowe Cooper. Photo by Don Allen.

ZH-ZI

BRU

25″ Bru Jne #10. She has a walking body, brown eyes, an elaborate costume and to top all that off, was a Blue Ribbon winner at the San Francisco Convention. This is an exceptional example of a closed mouth Bru. Courtesy Marlowe Cooper. Photo by Don Allen.

ZI-ZK

BRU

27″ Bru marked Jne 12. R. Ball jointed composition/wood body with closed mouth, pierced ears and set eyes. Courtesy Jeanne Haskins. Photo by Ted Long.

ZD-ZE

DANEL & CIE

21½" Paris Bebe marked Tete Dep/9. Composition jointed body. Closed mouth. Made by Danel & Cie. Courtesy Jeanne Haskins. Photo by Ted Long.

S-T

DANEL & CIE

21½" Paris Bebe/9. Composition jointed body. Closed mouth. Made by Danel & Cie. Courtesy Jeanne Haskins. Photo by Ted Long.
S-T

DANEL & CIE

Right: 28″ Paris Bebe/Depose, with identical mark on the body. Closed mouth. Made by Danel & Cie between 1889 and 1895. She is having tea with a wax friend who is 20″ tall and a poured wax with inset hair, cloth body and poured wax arms and legs. Courtesy Margaret McDonald. Photo by Ted Long.

T-U

DENAMUR, E.

16" Bebe Teteur. (Bru) Open mouth/nurser. Composition jointed body. 10" Marked: E. 2. D/Depose child; (Denamur) and the tiny, all original is marked: S.F.B.J. 60. Courtesy Jay Minter. Photo by Dwight Smith.

16" — Bru — Z-ZA
10" — E.D. — N-P
8" — S.F.B.J. — B-C

DENAMUR, E.

17″ Cousins. They both have open mouths and are on jointed composition bodies. Left is marked E.6 D./Depose (Denamur) and right is an F.G. (in scroll) child (F. Gaultier). Both courtesy Jay Minter. Photo by Dwight Smith.

17″ — E.D. — S-T
17″ — F.G. — T-U

DENAMUR, E.

22″ Socket head on fully jointed composition body. Open mouth, pierced ears. Marks; E.D./Depose. Courtesy Jay Minter. Toys from Ralph Minter Collection. Photo by Dwight Smith.
T-U

FERTÉ

Just as if she were found in an attic in New Orleans, this 12″ doll is marked B.F. and has a closed mouth and very deep crown slice. Made by FERTÉ, CA. 1875. Courtesy Jay Minter. Photo by Dwight Smith.

Q-S

FLEISCHMANN & BLODEL

20½" Eden Bébé with pierced ears, blue eyes and 6 teeth. Straight wrists on ball jointed body. Marks; Eden Bébé/Paris/9/Deposé. Made by Fleischmann & Blodel. Courtesy Burnice Wallen. Photo by Ted Long.

L-N

FRÈRES, MAY & CIE

21″ Bébé Mascotte that looks very much like a Jumeau. Head is incised with a "J" only. Ball jointed composition body. Closed mouth. Made by MAY FRÈRES CIE (1890). Courtesy Jeanne Haskins. Photo by Ted Long.

S-U

GAULTIER, F.

15½" F.G. child on a marked Gesland body. Closed mouth. Head is incised F.G. in scroll. Courtesy Jeanne Haskins. Photo by Ted Long.

V-X

GAULTIER, F.

16" Marked F 7 G with blue eyes and composition body with straight wrists. All original. Courtesy Jeanne Gregg. Photo by O. D. Gregg.

T-U

GAULTIER, F.

18" Marked with F.G. in scroll with closed mouth and composition body. The boy is unmarked and on a Schmitt & Fils body and has a closed, pouty mouth. Both courtesy of Karen Penner. Photo by Dwight Smith.

T-U

GAULTIER, F.

18″ Incised F.G., in scroll and with wooden shoulder plate. She is on a Gesland marked body and has an old costume and marked slippers. The eyes are blue and the mouth is closed. (Author) Photo by Don Allen.
X-Z

GAULTIER, F.

20″ Closed mouth F.G. in scroll. Composition body with straight wrists. Courtesy Jay Minter. Photo by Dwight Smith.

U-V

GAULTIER, F.

This is a closed mouth child that is marked F.G., in a scroll and from the collection of Cynthia Orgeron. Photo by Neil and William Venta.

22″ — U-V

GAULTIER, F.

25″ F.5 G. with portrait eyes. The ears are pierced and she has a human hair wig. The body has straight wrists and is marked Jumeau. She is wearing an old boy's walking dress of beige linen. Courtesy Jeanne Gregg. Photo by O. D. Gregg.

V-W

GAULTIER, F.

27″ Tete Jumeau with open mouth and ball jointed body is shown with a 25″ Bébé Gesland on the choice Gesland stockingette body with bisque lower arms. Closed mouth. Marked F.G. in scroll. Courtesy Louella Alvenslaben. Photo by Ted Long.

27″ — Jumeau — O-Q
25″ — F.G./Gesland — Z-ZA

GAULTIER, F.

31″ Marked F.G. in scroll with closed mouth and original clothes. The baby in the buggy is an 18″ with cloth body, composition arms and legs and is marked: Kiddie Joy/Germany. Baby made by Armand Marseille. Courtesy Margaret McDonald. Photo by Ted Long.

Y-Z

Kiddie Joy — F-H

H

13″ marked "H", on head. Blue eyes and human hair wig. Closed mouth. On fully jointed composition body and has pierced ears. Courtesy Jeanne Gregg. Photo by O. D. Gregg.

ZF-ZH

18″ Incised "H" #3 and is on a marked Jumeau body. Closed mouth, blue eyes and pierced ears. The dolls that are marked "H" or "A.T." are generally found only in very advanced collections as they are extremely rare and expensive. This beauty is in the collection of Marlowe Cooper. Photo by Don Allen.

ZH-ZK

JUMEAU

12" Early Jumeau Portrait on jointed composition body with straight wrists. Closed mouth and large expressive paperweight eyes. Original shoes, clothes replaced. No marks on head, body marked: Jumeau/Medaille D'or/Paris. Courtesy Jeanne Gregg. Photo by O. D. Gregg.

R-T

JUMEAU

12" Marked only 7 and has a look of a Jumeau. Fired color into the bisque, pierced ears and closed mouth with rosy lips. Black eyes and jointed body. All original except wig. The original wig is lambs wool and has fallen to pieces. Courtesy Marlowe Cooper. Photo by Don Allen.

U-V

JUMEAU

15″ Socket head on wood ball jointed body. Blue eyes and marked on head "S" or "5". Marks on body: Bébé Jumeau/Diplome D'Honneur, stamped in blue. Open mouth with six teeth. Courtesy Penny Pendlebury. Photo by Penny.

K-M

JUMEAU

17″ Closed mouth Jumeau with straight wrists. Unusual in that she is incised Depose /Jumeau, plus a painted on 8. The wig is original. (Author) Photo by Dwight Smith.

U-V

JUMEAU

17″ tall Jumeau with an open mouth and fully jointed composition body. She is marked Tete Jumeau and has a marked Jumeau body. Courtesy Jay Minter. Photo by Dwight Smith.

J-L

JUMEAU

18½″ Head is incised C/E.J. and the body is stamped Jumeau Medaille D'Or/Paris. Her clothes are all original and she came with a trunk with extra dresses and shoes. The wig is new. Courtesy Jill Koons. Photo by Penny Pendlebury.
U-V

JUMEAU

18¼″ E.J. Jointed composition body. Closed mouth. Body is marked: Trinaeau. Courtesy Jeanne Haskins. Photo by Ted Long. U-V

JUMEAU

19″ Jumeau with closed mouth and paperweight eyes. Composition jointed body. Marks; Tete Jumeau. (Author) Photo by Dwight Smith.

R-T

JUMEAU

Three sisters and all Jumeaus. Two are marked Tete Jumeau and the one with the black wig and maroon/black bonnet is marked 1906. All have open mouths. Courtesy Jay Minter. Photo by Dwight Smith.

16″ — I-K
20″ — J-L

JUMEAU

The first two are: 19″ Deposse/Tete Jumeau/Bte S.G.D.G./8 in original flowered dress with closed mouth and 20½″ unmarked Jumeau (has only a "v" made with a brush), who also has a closed mouth. They stand with a cousin who is 19″ tall, marked with an F.G. in a scroll. Closed mouth. All have ball jointed bodies. Courtesy Louella Alvenslaben. Photos by Ted Long.

19″ — Jumeau — R-T
19″ — F.G. — U-V
19″ — Unmarked — J-L

JUMEAU

19½″ Unmarked Jumeau on Jumeau body with full joints. Closed mouth and pierced ears. Courtesy Burnice Wallen. Photo by Ted Long.

J-L

20″ Jumeau that is incised E.J. Large paperweight brown eyes, closed mouth and applied ears. Courtesy Karen Penner. Photo by Dwight Smith.
U-W

JUMEAU

20″ Jumeau with large eyes and closed mouth. Marks; Bébé Jumeau. Courtesy Burnice Wallen. Photo by Ted Long.

R-T

JUMEAU

20″ Wire eye Jumeau. Jointed composition body. Open mouth and flirty eyes. Marks: Tete Jumeau (incised) red check mark/ Bte-SGDG. Courtesy Jeanne Haskins. Photo by Ted Long.
U-W

JUMEAU

20″ Tete Jumeau with blue eyes, pierced ears and human hair wig. She is marked Deposé Tete Jumeau BTE S.G.D.G. 8. Closed mouth and excellent quality bisque. Courtesy Jeanne Gregg. Photo by O. D. Gregg.

R-T

JUMEAU

The girl is a 22" Tete Jumeau with closed mouth and is from the collection of Delores Ward. The buggy is from the collection of Joy Muir. The baby is called "Laughing Jumeau" and was made by S.F.B.J. with mold number 236. Open/closed mouth with teeth. Courtesy Delores Ward. Photo by Neil & William Venta.

22" — T-U

18" S.F.B.J. 236 — N-P

JUMEAU

22½″ Bébé Jumeau with open mouth, on ball jointed body. Shown with original box. Courtesy Burnice Wallen. Photo by Ted Long.

M-O

JUMEAU

23″ Unmarked Jumeau. Open mouth. Typical Jumeau jointed body. Marked only with a 9. Courtesy Mary Partridge. Photo by Ted Long.

J-H

JUMEAU

All original Jumeau that is 25″ tall and has an open mouth, playing jacks with an S.F.B.J. 236 child with an open/closed mouth. Jumeau from the collection of Cynthis Orgeron. S.F.B.J. 236 belongs to Delores Ward. Photo by Neil & William Venta.

25″ — Jumeau — M-O
18″ S.F.B.J. 236 — N-P

JUMEAU

25″ E. J. Jumeau on fully jointed composition body. Large eyes and closed mouth. She is taking care of her little friend from Germany who is an intaglio eyed Kestner. Courtesy Ethel Stewart. Photo by Ted Long.

25″ E.J. — V-W

JUMEAU

26″ Tete Jumeau with closed mouth and straight wrists on a composition body. Large expressive eyes and with eyebrows that almost meet. Courtesy Ethel Stewart. Photo by Ted Long.

26″ — O-Q

JUMEAU

29″ Tete Jumeau Depose/Bte S.G.D.G. with closed mouth and original clothes. The baby in the sulky is a 21″ Dream Baby with cloth body and celluloid hands. Marked A.M./Germany/341/6. The mouth is closed. Courtesy Margaret McDonald. Photo by Ted Long.

29″ Jumeau — T-U

21″ — 341 — G-I

JUMEAU

Schmitt type body with "free formed" ball joints. These bodies are found marked Jumeau as well as on "Belton" type dolls. This head is marked: 192. These 192 heads seemed to have been made by Kestner for Jumeau. Open mouth. Courtesy Kathryn Fain.

20″ H-J

Shows a close up of the head on the 192 Kestner-Jumeau. Courtesy Kathryn Fain.

LADIES OF FASHION

16″ Smiling Fashion with swivel head on bisque shoulder plate. All wood, articulated jointed body. Came in trunk with extra dress, undies and nightie. Set cobalt blue eyes, pierced ears. Courtesy Jill Koons. Photo by Penny Pendlebury.

R-S

LADIES OF FASHION

In blue dress: 16″ Jumeau on wooden body. In white dress is a 16″ with twill covered, jointed body and is unmarked. The undressed doll is 13″ that is marked F.G. on shoulderplate and she is on a Gesland body. The screen was made for the 1976 Convention in San Francisco by Margaret McDonald. Dolls courtesy of Margaret McDonald. Photo by Ted Long.

16″ — Jumeau — P-R 16″ Twill — S-T
13″ — F.G. — R-S

LADIES OF FASHION

Marked: E 7 J. fashion. She is 17″ tall and on a fashion kid body with stitched toes and fingers. Swivel bisque head on bisque shoulder plate. Blue eyes, closed mouth and pierced ears. May be original. Courtesy Jeanne Gregg. Photo by O. D. Gregg.
T-U

LADIES OF FASHION

21″ Unmarked Fashion with bisque shoulder head (unjointed) Bisque arms and hands to elbow. Kid arms to shoulder, rest cloth body. Came in trunk and is holding her nightie and comb that came with her. All original, except wig. Set cobalt blue eyes and pale bisque. Courtesy Jill Koons. Photo by Penny Pendlebury.
S-T

LADIES OF FASHION

Fashion in red is marked only with a "D" and is from the collection of Cynthia Orgeron as is one in red marked F.G. The one in yellow is an F.G. and belongs to Delores Ward. Furniture from the collection of Joy Muir. Photo by Neil & William Venta.

16" — Red — L-N
16" — F.G. — K-M
12" — red/black — J-K

LADIES OF FASHION

This fashion doll has a fully articulated wood body with bisque head that was made by Jumeau. From the collection of Delores Ward. Photo by Neil & William Venta.
17½" — T-U

LADIES OF FASHION

This photo shows an unmarked little girl with glass eyes and a closed mouth, along with a marked F.G. fashion lady. The fashion belongs to Delores and child is in the collection of Cynthia Orgeron. Photo by Mary Elaine Lora.

11″ — F.G. — K-L

6″ — all bisque — C-E

LADIES OF FASHION

Marked on back of head "E". Jumeau fashion with blue eyes and pierced ears. Kid body with stitched toes and bisque lower arms. Old blonde wig. Socket head on bisque shoulder plate. Courtesy Jeanne Gregg. Photo by O. D. Gregg.

19″ — N-Q

LADIES OF FASHION

13″ Smiling Jumeau Fashion. Swivel head on bisque shoulder plate. On a half wood, half kid body. Her upper torso and arms are wood with articulated joints. All original. Marked: B, on shoulder plate. Courtesy Jill Koons. Photo by Penny Pendlebury.

13″ — K-M

MECHANICAL

Mechanical with baby. Measures 10″ tall when sitting. She feeds the baby with a bottle. Original. Courtesy Louella Alvenslaben. Photo by Ted Long.

Y-ZA

MECHANICAL

14" Mechanical Harp player. French Fashion head that is a flange joint. Dark lined eyes and closed mouth. Courtesy Louella Alvenslaben. Photo by Ted Long.

ZA-ZB

MECHANICAL

French mechanical marked Tete Jumeau. Wind up and all original. Stands on top of music box that plays two tunes. She lifts perfume bottle, moves head from side to side and raises handkerchief and nods head yes. Doll is 15″ tall and overall height is 19″. Courtesy Jeanne Gregg. Photo by O. D. Gregg.

ZA-ZB

MECHANICAL

French mechanical. Raises arm and looks into mirror. Key on stand winds up music box in base. Clothes are not original. Plays one tune. Bisque head marked: Tete Jumeau. Composition body, pierced ears. Courtesy Jeanne Gregg. Photo by O. D. Gregg.

Redressed: V-X
Original: Z-ZA

MECHANICAL

Mechanical Nurse Maid and baby. Nurse Maid leans forward as baby raises. Courtesy Burnice Wallen. Photo by Ted Long.

Z-ZA

RABERY & DELPHIEU

15″ R.D. on ball jointed composition body. Closed mouth. Head incised: R-2-O.D. Made by Rabery & Delphieu. Courtesy Jeanne Haskins. Photo by Ted Long.

15″ — Q-S

RABERY & DELPHIEU

The shorter doll is marked: R.D. with open mouth and on jointed composition body. Made by Rabery & Delphieu. She belongs to Delores Ward. The taller doll is an unmarked Jumeau that only has a "6" on her head. The beautiful box belongs to Joy Muir. The unmarked Jumeau is from the collection of Cynthia Orgeron. Photo by Neil & William Venta.

17" — R.D. — S-T

25" — Unmarked — L-N

SCHMITT & FILS

15″ Schmitt. Jointed body of composition and wood with straight wrists. Closed mouth. Marks: 

Courtesy Jeanne Haskins. Photo by Ted Long.

15″ — W-Y

SCHMITT & FILS

16½″ Schmitt with composition body with straight wrists. Marked with shield. Closed mouth. 16″ marked: Tete Deposse/Paris Bebe/6. (in red) with ball jointed body. Courtesy Louella Alvenslaben. Photo by Ted Long.

16½″ — U-W

16½″ — W-Y

SCHMITT & FILS

22½″ Schmitt. Composition body with large "free form" balls at joints. Very flat on backside and long fingers. Closed mouth. Marks:

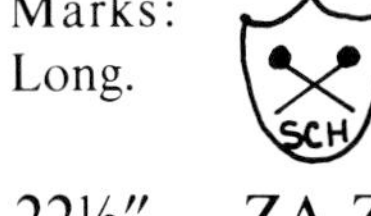

Courtesy Burnice Wallen. Photo by Ted Long.

22½″ — ZA-ZC

SCHMITT & FILS

23″ Closed mouth and large set eyes. Free formed balls at joints with very flat bottom side with the marks of a shield and crossed hammers. Head is marked with the same shield/hammers: 

(Author) Photo by Dwight Smith.

23″ — ZA-ZC

SCHMITT & FILS

23″ Marked 103/DEP. on head and has a marked Schmitt body: Full closed mouth with deeper red line between lips. These dolls still remain a mystery and even if the heads are most certainly made in Germany, they are sold as a French doll. (Author) Photo by Dwight Smith.

L-N

S.F.B.J.

10" Five piece body with painted, molded shoes and sox. Painted eyes, original and marked: S.F.B.J./20/Paris/12. Courtesy Mary Partridge. Photo by brother.

C-D

S.F.B.J.

12½" Black fired in color, incised Paris, S.F.B.J. 52. Brown body and head are mache (not composition) and the body is that of a toddler. The black eyes sleep but are turned upward. The mouth is open/closed with four painted upper teeth. Courtesy Marlowe Cooper. Photo by Don Allen.

ZD-ZF

S.F.B.J.

12″ Marked S.F.B.J. 60 with sleep eyes and an open mouth. All original. Courtesy Mary Partridge. Photo by brother.

C-E

S.F.B.J.

This French boy is marked: 227-Paris. He does not have the S.F.B.J. mark but is just like the ones that are so marked. Painted, molded hair and blue "jewel" set eyes. The mouth is open/closed with molded upper teeth. He is 14" tall, and is on French jointed body. Courtesy Jeanne Gregg. Photo by O. D. Gregg.

P-R

S.F.B.J.

Left to right: S.F.B.J. 301 Paris 30″ on ball jointed body with original clothes — open mouth. Sitting is S.F.B.J. 251 Paris 12″ with ball jointed body. 18″ S.F.B.J. 236 with open/closed mouth. *Sitting:* S.F.B.J. 238 Paris that is 21½″ Open mouth and jewel eyes. S.F.B.J. 230 Paris that is 31″ on ball jointed body. Last doll is marked E. 8 D. and is 19″. Ball jointed body. Original. Steiff cats. Courtesy Louella Alvenslaben. Photo by Ted Long.

19″ — E.D. — T-U
30″-31″ — O-Q
12″ — K-M
18″ — S-T
21½″— N-P

S.F.B.J.

23″ Socket head on fully jointed composition body. Pierced ears, open mouth and sleep eyes. Marks: S.F.B.J./230/Paris, in circle. Courtesy Kathy Walter. Photo by Dwight Smith.

L-N

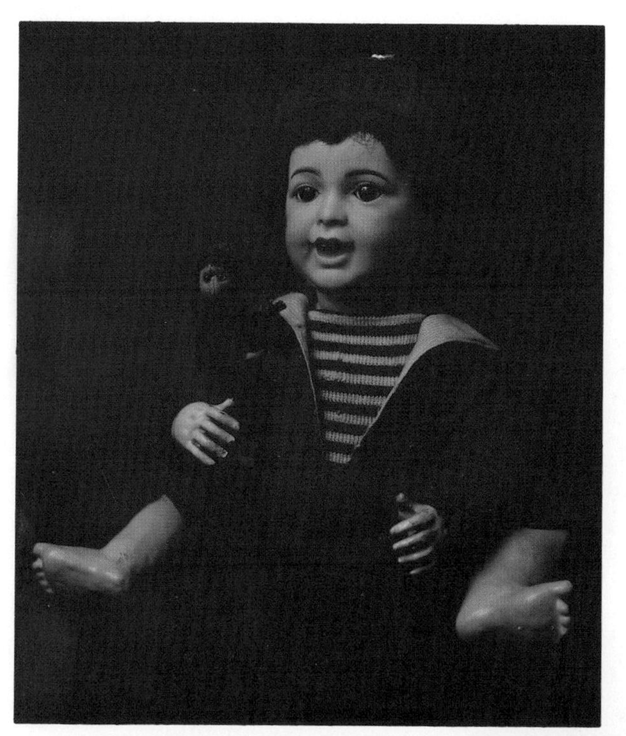

S.F.B.J.

17″ S.F.B.J. 236 with an open/closed mouth and on a composition toddler body. Courtesy Burnice Wallen. Photo by Ted Long.

S-T

18″ S.F.B.J. 236 Paris with open/closed mouth and on a fully jointed composition body. Courtesy Louella Alvenslaben. Photo by Ted Long.

S-T

S.F.B.J.

26″ S.F.B.J. 236 boy with open/closed mouth and molded teeth. Courtesy Jay Minter. Photo by Dwight Smith. 15″ S.F.B.J. 236 girl with open/closed mouth and molded upper teeth. Courtesy Jeanne Gregg. Photo by O. D. Gregg.

15″ — O-Q
26″ — T-U

S.F.B.J.

21½" S.F.B.J. 238 Paris. Has open mouth, ball jointed body and "jewel eyes". The child is riding a Steiff pony that is very rare. Courtesy Louella Alvenslaben. Photo by Ted Long.

Q-S

S.F.B.J.

13½" #239/Poulbot (in script) This doll came on two different type bodies, jointed and straight legs. Full closed mouth, brown eyes and is all original. These "street urchins" that are all original apparently all had red wigs. Courtesy Marlowe Cooper. Photo by Don Allen.

Z-ZB

S.F.B.J.

8″ Incised S.F.B.J. Paris 245. He has blue glass eyes that are to the side. Original clothes and body, which has brown painted slippers and white sox. Open/closed mouth with four painted teeth. This doll is also seen with three painted teeth. Courtesy Marlowe Cooper. Photo by Don Allen.
Z-ZC

S.F.B.J.

18″ On toddler body that is jointed, composition. Has blue sleep eyes and an open/closed mouth with two molded upper teeth. Marks; 21/S.F.B.J./247/Paris/8. Courtesy Jill Koons. Photo Penny Pendlebury.

S-T

S.F.B.J.

S.F.B.J. toddler with mold number 247. She has an open/closed mouth with two inset upper teeth. She is shown with her Schoenhut friends and in the garden of her owner, Jeanne Cregg.

P-R

These children are 17½″ and 18″ tall with set eyes and composition bodies. Left holding Grandpa is marked: S.F.B.J. 247 Paris. The one holding Grandma is marked: Unis/France in an oval/247/71 149. Courtesy Jeanne Gregg. Photo by O. D. Gregg.

S.F.B.J. — 247 — S-T

Unis — 247 — O-Q

S.F.B.J.

18″ S.F.B.J. 252 #10 pouty. Original marked body. This is one of the 200 series made by S.F.B.J. and these dolls could make a collection by themselves. Courtesy Marlowe Cooper. Photo by Don Allen.

W-Y

S.F.B.J.

18″ S.F.B.J. 301 with blue set eyes and blonde human hair wig. She is a wind up mechanical walker and is wearing old clothes. Courtesy Jeanne Gregg. Photo by O. D. Gregg.
J-L

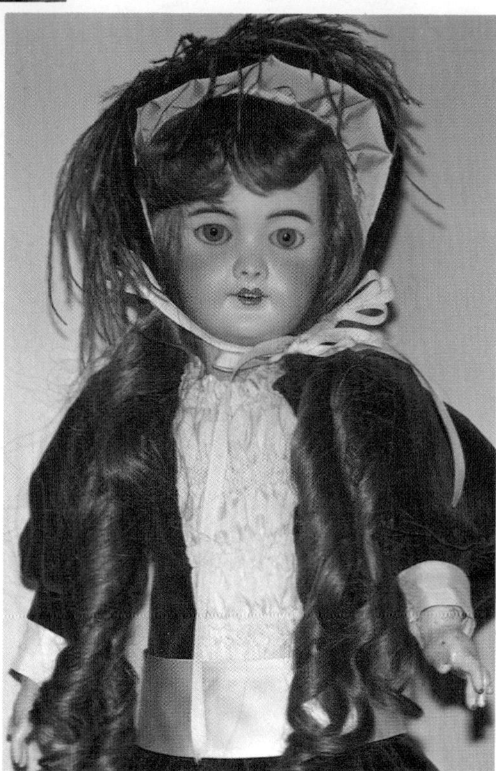

26″ Marked S.F.B.J. 301 with sleep eyes and an open mouth. Fully jointed composition body. Courtesy Mary Partridge. Photo by brother.
J-L

S.F.B.J.

Both these children are S.F.B.J.s. Both have open mouths and sleep eyes. The one in pink belongs to Cynthia Orgeron and the other to Mary Nutt & Sherry Garcia. The cat is celluloid and also Cynthia's and the dog is a Steiff. Photo by Mary Elaine Lora.

25″ — J-L
18″ — H-J

STEINER, JULES

11″ All original Steiner. Closed mouth, pierced ears and brown eyes. Mache body with straight wrists. Marked: J. Steiner/BTE S.G.D.G./Paris/Fre A-3. Body is marked Medaille D'Or/Paris. Courtesy Jeanne Gregg. Photo by O. D. Gregg.

Q-S

STEINER, JULES

17″ Crying Jules Steiner. When wound with key, the doll kicks and the head turns from side to side. Wood/composition/mache and cloth body and limbs. Open mouth with two rows teeth, referred to as "fish teeth". Courtesy Burnice Wallen. Photo by Ted Long.

R-T

STEINER, JULES

21" Bourgion Steiner. Typical Steiner body with short stubby finger and separate large toe. Mache/composition boy. Closed mouth. Courtesy Ethel Stewart. Photo by Ted Long.

X-Z

STEINER, JULES

21″ Steiner that is all original. Closed mouth and marked: J.Steiner /BTE S.G.D.G./Paris/Fire A-13. Courtesy Jay Minter. Photo by Dwight Smith.

U-V

STEINER, JULES

21" Jules Steiner with ball jointed body with unjointed wrist. Closed mouth. Marks: J.Steiner/B.V.S.G.D.G./Paris/Fi re A 15. Courtesy Louella Alvenslaben. Photo by Ted Long.

U-V

STEINER, JULES

23″ Bourgoin Steiner marked J. Steiner Bte S.G.D.G. Sie C 3 J. Bourgoin St. Closed mouth. Original clothes and wig restyled. (Author) Photo by Dwight Smith.

X-Z

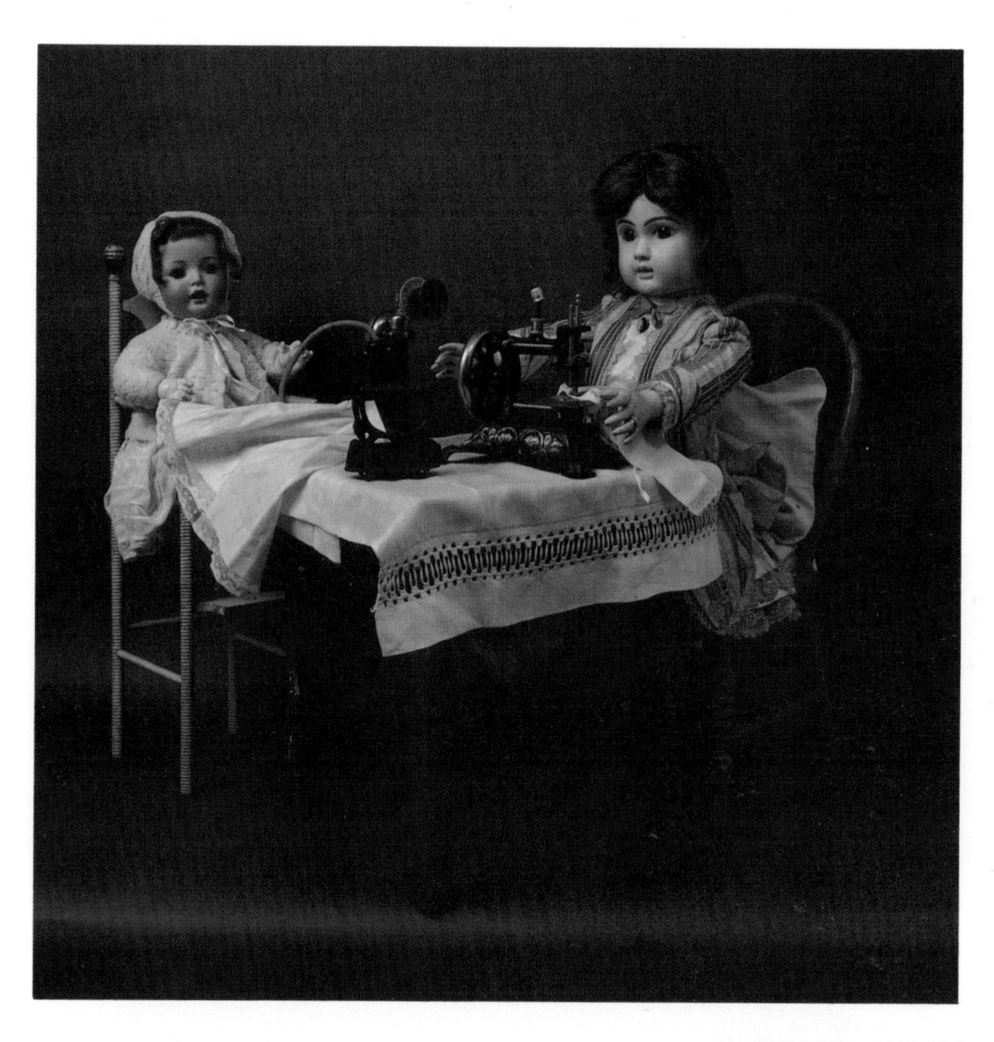

STEINER, JULES

29″ marked: J. Steiner/Bte S.G.D.G./Paris/Fi re A 19. The baby in high chair is 16″ tall and marked: S PB H, in a star H/Hanna and was made by Schoneau and Hoffmeister. Courtesy Margaret McDonald. Photo by Ted Long.

29″ — V-X

Hanna — D-F

STEINER, JULES

34″ Marked: J. Steiner Bte S.G.D.G. Sie C 7 J. Bourgoin St. All on one row at the top of the head. These Stieners are called Bourgion Stieners and they are much more rare than the A Series Stieners. The baby in buggy is a 22″ "Kaiser" baby marked K star R/100. Courtesy Margaret McDonald. Photo by Ted Long.

34″ — Z-ZB

THUILLIER, A.

15" A 5 T. incised high on head. The ears are pierced and applied. The mouth is closed with white line between lips. Original mache body with unjointed wrists. Wears original A.T. marked slippers. Courtesy Marlowe Cooper. Photo by Don Allen.

ZE-ZG

THUILLIER, A.

23" Incised A 11 T high on head. Blue eyes and applied, pierced ears. Closed mouth and jointed body, including wrists. Old costume and bonnet. From the collection of Marlowe Cooper. Photo by Don Allen.

ZK-ZM

THUILLIER, A.

25″ A 12 T, incised. Brown eyes and jointed mache body with large hands. Old costume and bonnet, that may be original. The ears are pierced and applied. Was a Red Ribbon winner at the 1977 National Convention in San Diego. Courtesy Marlowe Cooper. Photo by Don Allen.

ZL-ZN

UNIS

7″ Unis France with unusual face. Paper weight eyes. Bisque head on mache body. Original. Painted on shoes. Open mouth. Courtesy Ethel Stewart. Photo by Ted Long.

C-E

UNIS

12" With painted eyes and on a five piece body with painted on shoes and hose. She is marked: Unis, in an oval/60. Courtesy Jay Minter. Photo by Dwight Smith.

C-E

UNIS

21½" Socket head with original black human hair wig, blue sleep eyes with long black human hair lashes. Open mouth/ five teeth, composition body and marked: Unis France, in oval/301. She stands with an unsigned oil painting dating about 1890-1900. Doll and photo courtesy Clarice Kemper.

G-H

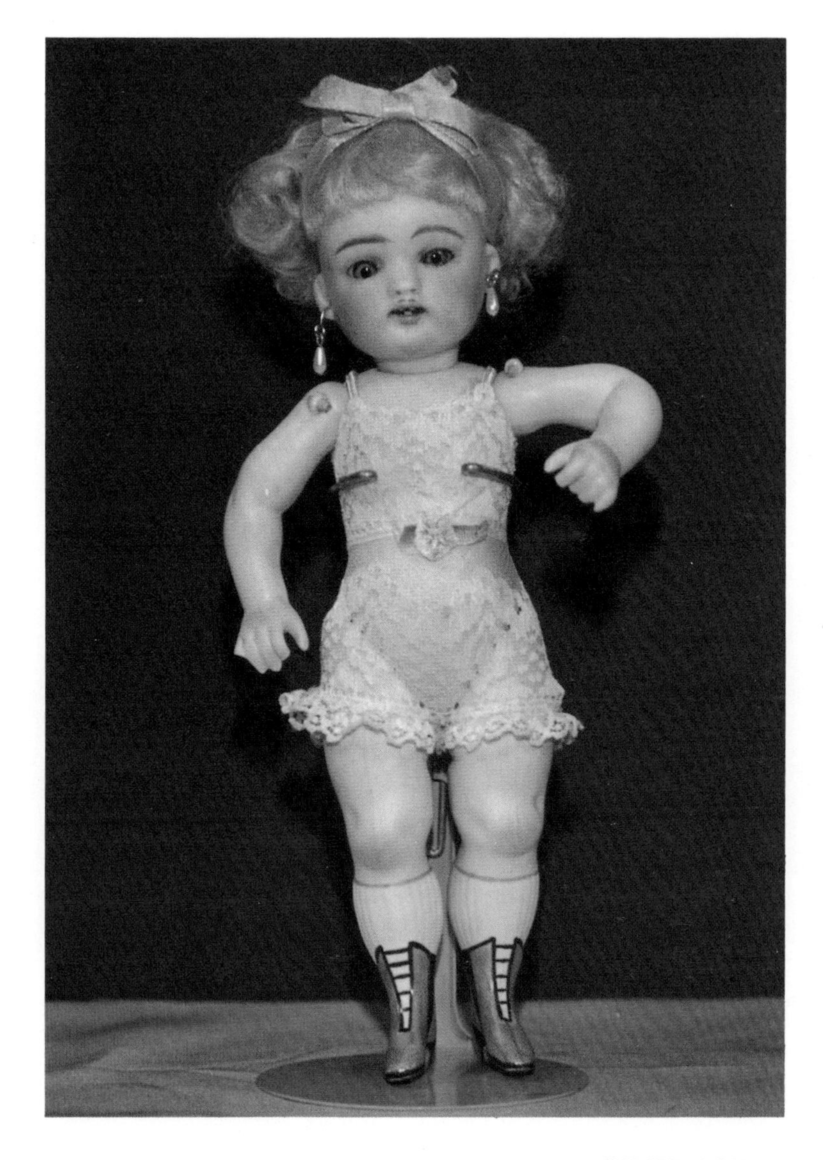

UNKNOWN

8½" All bisque called the "French Wrestler". Original mohair wig, painted on yellow and black boots. Blue sleep eyes and in original lace "Teddy". Courtesy Jeanne Gregg. Photo O. D. Gregg.
J-L

UNKNOWN

French all bisque boy and girl. Marked: 132/9. All original. Inset glass eyes. Closed mouths. Jointed at neck, shoulders and hips. Courtesy Jeanne Gregg. Photo O. D. Gregg.

E-G

UNKNOWN

13½" All celluloid. Socket head with closed mouth and painted blue eyes. Right arm is bent at elbow. She is jointed at the shoulders and hips. Painted on socks and shoes. Marks on head: Head of Eagle/ France/35. Doll and photo courtesy Penny Pendlebury.

A-B

UNKNOWN

16½" Unmarked French child. Kid body with bisque head on bisque shoulder plate (Swivel neck). Closed mouth. Courtesy Jeanne Haskins. Photo by Ted Long.

N-Q

UNKNOWN

19″ Mache/wood French body. Paperweight eyes. Wide open/closed mouth/pierced ears and slight cheek dimples. Marks; 224/Dep, on head. Corset: Aux Sultanes/Rue Alsace Lorraine 13/En face le musee/Toulouse. (Author) Photo Dwight Smith.

M-O

UNKNOWN

19″ with kid body with gussets and bisque lower arms. Closed mouth and paperweight eyes. Marks: 8, at top of head and base of neck. Doll and photo courtesy Kathryn Fain.

M-O

UNKNOWN

Left is 19″ that is unmarked and resembles an A. Margue. Closed mouth and ears are not pierced. The quality of the bisque is poor. Right is a 27″ S.F.B.J. clown in factory original clothes and marked Bebe Eden slippers. The head and body are mache. He is shown in 1910 magazines. Courtesy Marlowe Cooper. Photo by Don Allen.

19″ — M-O
27″ — T-V

UNKNOWN

23″ Color fired into bisque and marked on head and body: Jumeau. Slightly open mouth, pierced ears and colored, jointed body. Lovely old costume, bonnet and marked shoes. Courtesy Marlowe Cooper. Photo Don Allen.

U-W

UNKNOWN

25″. Head is marked only with "12" and body is marked Jumeau Medaille D'or Paris. She is 25″ tall with applied ears that are pierced and has brown paperweight eyes. Courtesy Jeanne Gregg. Photo by O. D. Gregg.

T-U

BUGGIES

Beautiful wicker buggy of the Victorian Era. Courtesy Roberta Lago. Photo by Ted Long.

F-H

BUGGIES

English wooden coach with a German mache doll. Adjustable surrey. Courtesy Louella Alvenslaben. Photo by Ted Long.

H-J

BUGGIES

Large wheeled wicker buggy holding a baby that is a K Star R 127 that is 18″ tall. Courtesy Ethel Stewart. Photo by Ted Long.

E-G

18″ Baby — D-F

INDEX

Numbers

Letters

Symbols